Contents

Introduction

Contents

Overview

***Construction site safety* covers all aspects of current health, safety and environment issues in the building and construction industry. It is designed to help managers, supervisors and small businesses understand how they should comply with, and put into practice, their legal, moral and social responsibilities.**

Construction site safety (GE 700)

Construction site safety is a leading publication within the construction industry, based on current construction health, safety and environment legislation, guidance and good practice. It will assist in the crucial areas of:

- ☑ construction site set up and management
- ☑ management of occupational ill health
- ☑ accident prevention and investigation
- ☑ environmental good practice.

The content has been written with the site manager in mind, with a balance between outlining the requirements of relevant legislation and providing practical guidance on how to comply.

The content of *Construction site safety*, which is developed with construction industry experts, is revised annually to take into account the latest changes in legislation and new or updated health, safety and environment industry guidance and good practice.

Construction site safety is supported by a companion website that keeps users informed of legislation changes, content updates and links to further guidance *(refer to Companion website on page 9)*.

Construction site safety is also available to purchase online or on CD-ROM.

Construction site safety is the official supporting publication for the *Site management safety training scheme* (SMSTS), a five-day course for construction site managers, which covers the content of Sections A to D. Section E is the official supporting publication for the Site Safety Plus *Site environmental awareness training scheme* (SEATS), a one-day course for construction site supervisors and managers.

Acknowledgements

CITB wishes to acknowledge the assistance offered by the following organisations in the preparation of this edition of GE 700:

- ☑ Britannia Safety and Training
- ☑ Cleehill Plant Ltd
- ☑ Construction Plant-hire Association
- ☑ Costain
- ☑ Construction Industry Scaffolders' Record Scheme (CISRS)
- ☑ Crossrail
- ☑ Drilling and Sawing Association
- ☑ Environment Agency
- ☑ Eurovia UK
- ☑ Gas Safe Consultants Ltd
- ☑ Green Construction Board
- ☑ Health and Safety Executive
- ☑ Henry Boot Construction Ltd
- ☑ Hire Association Europe
- ☑ International Powered Access Federation (IPAF)
- ☑ Lead Paint Safety Association
- ☑ MJ Fuller and Associates
- ☑ Morgan Sindall
- ☑ Mount Anvil
- ☑ National Access and Scaffolding Confederation (NASC)
- ☑ Norse Energy Ltd
- ☑ National Construction College
- ☑ National Federation of Builders
- ☑ National Federation of Demolition Contractors
- ☑ NHBC
- ☑ Nick Price Carpentry Services
- ☑ Persimmon Homes
- ☑ R&D Construction Ltd
- ☑ Simian Risk Management Ltd
- ☑ Skanska
- ☑ Thames Laboratories
- ☑ UK Green Building Council
- ☑ Unite the Union
- ☑ Vernon Watson – Institute of Demolition Engineers
- ☑ Willmott Dixon

Work-related injuries and ill health statistics for the construction industry

Approximately 2.54 million people are employed in the UK construction industry. It covers activities including housing, utilities, repair and maintenance, refurbishment, demolition, roofing, shopfitting, mechanical and electrical, plumbing and highways maintenance.

It is made up of about 193,000 businesses, of which 90% employ fewer than 10 workers.

Although construction accounts for only 5% of the employers in Britain it accounts for 31% of fatal injuries to employers and 10% of reported major or specified injuries.

Construction workers (just like you) could die due to work-related ill health, or as a result of an accident, if control measures are not followed.

On average 46 workers are killed each year due to accidents. In 2013-14 there were 42 fatal injuries to workers, with 14 of these to the self-employed. There was also four fatal injuries to members of the public. The biggest killer (around half) is due to falls from height. Over the last 10 years 46 members of the public have lost their lives as a result of construction related injuries. These tend to be as a result of falls, slips and trips, or being struck by vehicles. On average seven people die each year as a result of falling through fragile roofs.

Each year there are about 2,457 major injuries (such as broken bones, fractured skull and amputations) and 3,293 over seven-day injuries.

The most common over seven-day injuries are due to manual handling, slips, trips and falls on the same level, falls from height and being struck by an object.

The health and safety statistics for 2013-14 show there were an estimated 76,000 cases of work-related ill health, of which 31,000 were new cases. An estimated 2.3 million working days were lost; 1.7 million due to ill health and 592,000 due to workplace injury, making a total of 1.1 days lost per worker.

The construction industry has the largest burden of occupational cancer. Over 40% of occupational cancer deaths and registrations involved people who worked in construction.

There has been a substantial reduction in the number of fatalities in the last 40 years. However, the most significant carcinogen is past exposure to asbestos (69%), followed by silica (17%) and painting and diesel engine exhausts (6-7%).

Approximately 5,000 people die each year due to past exposure to asbestos.

Work-related respiratory disease covers a range of illnesses that are caused or made worse by breathing in hazardous substances (such as construction dust) that damage the lungs.

In 2005 it was estimated that 500 people died from silica-related lung diseases (dust from cutting blocks, kerbs, and so on). Many more suffer from occupational asthma or are forced to leave the industry due to work-related ill health.

Vibration white finger, carpal tunnel syndrome, occupational deafness and dermatitis are the most common non-lung diseases suffered by those in the construction industry.

www. **For further information refer to the HSE website.**

Why so many accidents?

Reports of present day construction accidents and ill health make depressing reading because simple actions were not taken to prevent them. In many cases, those planning the jobs totally failed to consider the health, safety or welfare of the people carrying out the work (and possibly others who were affected) and to actively manage the situation.

Common examples of such events include:

- the increasing number of workers who suffer from cancers and life changing illnesses from breathing and skin complaints – some of these force the sufferer to give up work, because exposure to dangerous substances, such as dust, are not even considered, let alone prevented or controlled
- the deaths and serious injuries that occur because people fall from height – often basic actions (like using temporary work platforms on fragile roofs, installing edge protection or using a safety harness and lanyard clipped to a strong point) were simply not taken
- workers being buried in collapsed excavations because the sides were unstable or not supported
- workers being killed or injured by construction plant because pedestrians were not kept out of the plant operating area.

Achieving a reasonable standard of on-site health and safety is not difficult. Where the work to be carried out is relatively uncomplicated and familiar, the precautions that need to be taken are, in many cases, simple and common sense, or may require just a little investigation or reading. The crucial decision for anyone with responsibility for on-site health and safety is to know when they have reached the limits of their knowledge and capabilities and therefore need the assistance of someone with specialist knowledge.

Caution should also be exercised when a job is not going to plan and there is the temptation to resort to improvised methods of working. If the person in control is not at ease with the way that things are going they should stop the job, step back and think things through carefully before deciding upon a course of action.

Research from the Health and Safety Executive (HSE) has shown that workers are most vulnerable during their first few days on site.

Accident statistics

Between April 2013 and March 2014 133 workers were fatally injured throughout the UK. In comparison 150 fatalities occurred in the same reporting period the previous year.

The overall fatality rate has dropped to 0.44 per 100,000 workers. This compares to an average of 0.56 for the previous five years.

In 2013-14 there were 42 fatal injuries to workers in construction – 9% lower than the annual average (46). The latest rate of fatal injury is 1.98 per 100,000 workers, compared to a five year average of 2.07.

Judith Hackitt, the HSE Chair, said:

> **... behind every number is the reality of a real person being killed or suffering injuries or ill health while simply doing their job.**
>
> **We should remind ourselves that last year someone went out to work and either did not return home to their loved ones or their loved ones came home with life changing injuries. The health and safety numbers also demonstrate the scale of harm being done to people's health while at work, too often leading to premature death.**

Setting out

Construction is an exciting industry. It is constantly changing as projects move on and jobs get done. As a result of this a building site is one of the most dangerous environments to work in.

But many accidents that occur on sites can be avoided if everyone on site works together. So a free film *Setting out* explains what the site must do and what you must do to stay healthy and safe at work.

This film is essential viewing for everyone involved in construction, and should be watched before sitting the CITB *Health, safety and environment test*. The principles of the film form the basis for the behavioural case study questions, which became a new element of the test in 2012. The test has been refreshed for 2015 to reflect the changes to the Construction (Design and Management) Regulations.

For further information or to view *Setting out* refer to the companion website: citb.co.uk/GE700companion.

Working Well Together

The Working Well Together (WWT) campaign is an industry-led initiative that helps support micro and small businesses improve their health and safety performance. WWT has become the most successful health and safety initiative within the construction industry. The campaign undertakes a variety of work, including health and safety awareness days, designer awareness days, breakfast and evening events, roadshows and regional WWT groups.

The aims of the WWT initiative are to:

- improve health and safety knowledge and good practice and seek to continuously improve health, safety and welfare performance in the construction industry
- provide practical advice and assistance to the construction industry on the provision and maintenance of healthy and safe working environments
- encourage co-operation between members in relation to sharing knowledge of health and safety matters
- promote training and learning in health and safety
- provide free or low cost information, advice and training to employers and workers in the construction industry
- stage events where at least half the people who attend will be from small businesses (15 or fewer employees) and 20% from micro businesses (five or fewer employees).

Working Well Together campaign posters

To find out how the WWT campaign can help you and your company refer to its website.

HSE construction division

The construction division of the HSE has a three year plan of work, which has been extended by a further year (2014-15). It is now more closely aligned to the overall HSE strategic plan.

The plan re-affirms the HSE's commitment to improving health and safety in the construction industry, by targeting high risk sectors and activities, and by continuing to work with industry partners, to deliver a variety of initiatives and products to help you and your business understand how to meet your legal obligations.

If you are visited by an HSE inspector it is likely they will be looking at some of the construction activities listed below.

Plan of work 2014-15

The plan of work sets out the construction division's work for 2014-15. This builds on previous work and continues the HSE's mission to deliver and, where possible, accelerate long-term improvements in the industry's health and safety performance, while making best use of their resources.

In 2014-15 and beyond **occupational disease and ill health** are a priority. They will be significantly increasing their focus on preventing occupational ill health, including respiratory risks, hand-arm vibration and occupational cancers, across all sectors of the industry.

They will also be looking beyond the site gate, examining how other duty holders (such as designers and clients) have, and can, influence health and safety standards on site.

www. **For the full *Plan of work* refer to the HSE website.**

Construction operational activities

The main operational activities will target the following.

- ☑ Licensed asbestos removal work.
- ☑ Small sites and projects.
- ☑ Refurbishment.
- ☑ Major projects and large contractors and clients.
- ☑ Local priorities.

Any areas of concern, with the potential to cause a catastrophic event, identified during a site visit will be addressed. The following five generic issues will also be considered, where appropriate, during site visits.

- ☑ Work at height.
- ☑ Occupational health risks.
- ☑ Asbestos risk.
- ☑ Provision of welfare facilities.
- ☑ Site conditions (good order).

In addition, the HSE will also consider the following.

Management of health risks	Raising awareness, promoting knowledge and ensuring control of health risks in construction.
Leadership	How effective directors and other senior managers are at leading health and safety and how work is supervised from the top of the organisation to the workforce.
Worker involvement	Encouraging effective worker involvement, so every worker plays an active role.
Contractor competence	Placing particular emphasis on the competence of organisations and individuals.
Temporary works	Raising awareness of managing temporary works effectively and ensuring that adequate arrangements are in place.
CDM duty holders	Examine the roles of duty holders (such as designers and clients) to determine their influence on the standards found on site.

Specific topics will include the following.

Concentrated health initiatives	To raise awareness and ensure compliance, including the year's refurbishment initiative (launched in September/October).
Fragile roofs	To ensure risks associated with working on or near fragile materials are adequately planned and controlled. The client's role in such work will be closely looked at.
Home building	Inspect home build sites and ensure that risks to health and safety are being effectively managed.
Loft conversion	Inspect the work and health and asbestos risks, and provide information events for those undertaking the work. A busy builder sheet will be produced to help small builders.
Solar panel installation on commercial premises	They will inspect the work and examine the client's role and provide information events so that those undertaking work know the standards expected.
Improving leadership performance	The HSE inspection teams will run a number of briefing events for local construction businesses to demonstrate the benefits of using the leadership and worker involvement toolkit (available on HSE website) and encourage them to use it.
Large contractors	Engage with a number of large contractor businesses at board level to encourage improved performance in the areas of leadership and supervision, occupational health management, avoiding catastrophe, emerging from recession and worker involvement.
Major projects	Continue to engage with clients or major projects to provide intervention plans on projects of significant interest.
Temporary demountable structures	Continue their work to examine the standard of safety management during the erection and dismantling of temporary demountable structures in the events and entertainments industry.
Fire (timber-frame structures)	Continue to work to ensure due regard is being paid to the UK Timber Frame Association (UKFTA) guidance during the development of timer-frame structures.

Enabling activities

The construction division will continue to work with the main stakeholders and intermediaries. Important areas of collaboration are shown below.

- ☑ Supporting the Working Well Together (WWT) campaign in raising awareness of health and safety issues within micro and small construction business, and supporting new groups to deliver at least 60 events during 2014-15, creating new groups when the opportunity arises.
- ☑ Developing a simpler and more easily understood revised regulatory package to replace the Construction (Design and Management) Regulations 2007.
- ☑ Finalising a review of the agreement for collaboration between the HSE and the Building Control Alliance.
- ☑ Working with industry stakeholders to identify channels through which guidance and important messages can be delivered to small sites.
- ☑ With industry partners developing guidance to support the Construction (Design and Management) regulatory package.

Summary

This plan reaffirms the construction division's commitment to improving health and safety in the construction industry by targeting high risk sectors and activities.

The HSE will continue to work with industry partners to deliver initiatives and products to assist businesses to understand and comply with their legal duties. They recognise they cannot achieve the improvements alone and look to all those in the construction industry to be part of the solution to bring about change and improvements in health and safety performance.

How to use GE 700

Contents

Overview

The following information sets out how to use *Construction site safety* and provides information on specific aspects, such as augmented reality and interactive forms. It also explains the companion website, which is a significant addition for keeping users informed of legislation changes, content updates and links to further guidance.

Construction site safety structure

Construction site safety is divided into the standard structure that is used across all core CITB publications.

Section A: Legal and management

Section B: Health and welfare

Section C: General safety

Section D: High risk activities

Section E: Environment

Section F: Specialist activities

Within *Construction site safety* each section is contained within a separate book, which has been designed to provide simple navigation for the user.

There is also an additional supporting book:

Section G: Checklists and forms.

This section is a collection of information that can be used on a day-to-day basis when running a site. The forms and checklists within Section G follow the same structure as in Sections A to F.

How to navigate

There are different ways to find the information you require within the sections. You can use the:

- ☑ initial contents pages at the start of each section
- ☑ more detailed chapter contents list
- ☑ index at the end of each section (but there is no index within Section G)
- ☑ new quick reference guide within this supporting information guide.

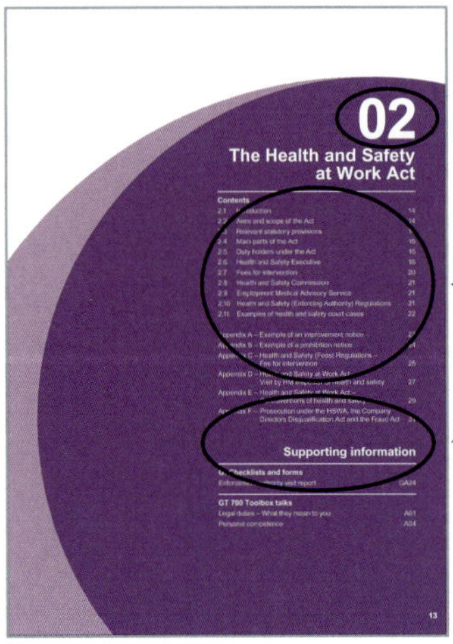

Chapters have been numbered to make movement around the sections easier. Therefore, chapter one of Section A is numbered 01, chapter two of Section B is numbered 02 and so on. However, references to chapters within other sections will be referred to as A01, B02, and so on.

Each chapter contains a contents list at the beginning.

The chapter contents lists will, where relevant, also contain references to any Section G: *Checklists and forms* or GT 700 *Toolbox talks*, that support the chapter topic and that you may find a useful source of further reference.

Use of icons

A set of icons emphasises important points within the text and also directs readers to further information. The icons are explained below.

Website/further info	Important	Case study
Example	Good practice	Quote
Question	Poor practice	Definition
Ideas	Caution	Checklist
Notes	Consultation	Video
Favourite	Guidance	Shopping basket

Companion website

The companion website is a free resource that can be used to support the reader in progressing from the GE 700 book content to additional information available on the internet. Instead of having to type long website details into browsers, or searching on appropriate terms, the reader is directed to the companion website where all other sites of interest can be accessed by quick links.

The companion website supports *Construction site safety* and it contains up to date information on:

- the current edition of each section (book)
- news (such as legislation changes, industry guidance and good practice)
- any minor amendments or updates to the current edition
- web-links, phone numbers and addresses.

This icon indicates that further information (such as useful websites and links) can be found on the companion website at citb.co.uk/GE700companion

The companion website will be regularly updated, to ensure that relevant information is current.

Save the companion website address to your favourites, so it is always available when you need It.

Rather than printing individual web-links in each section, which can become out of date, the relevant website will be stated alongside the icon (for example, for more information refer to the CITB website). The actual web-link can then be found on the companion website, referenced to the relevant section and chapter.

Steps to access a link

The content on the companion website is structured in the same way as the current edition of GE 700. To access information from a link in a book use the following steps to navigate the structure.

The example provided below is for the **drinkaware alcohol unit calculator** referenced in **B04 – 4.6 Alcohol**.

Step 1	Open the companion website	citb.co.uk/GE700companion
Step 2	Open the relevant section for the content required	**B: Health and welfare**
Step 3	Open the relevant chapter	**B04 Drugs and alcohol**
Step 4	Select the relevant link	**4.6 Alcohol unit calculator**
Step 5	Access the 3rd party referenced site	Alcohol unit calculator site opens

Interactive checklists and forms

For GE 700 users that have purchased a digital version of GE 700/15 (CD-ROM or online), all the checklists and forms included in Section G are available to download and use on site.

This enables you to complete individual or multiple forms on your computer before saving or printing them to use, as required. The forms are compatible with both PC and Mac operating systems. You can also print off blank copies of the forms and fill them in manually, if required.

The checklists and forms are user-friendly and quick to complete, making the recording of important information a simple process.

If you have not yet purchased a digital version of GE 700 refer to Section G of the companion website to trial an interactive form.

Augmented reality

What is augmented reality?

Augmented reality (AR) is cutting-edge technology. It provides layers of digital information (videos, photographs, sounds) simply by downloading an app and using the camera and sensors in your smartphone or tablet.

This technology has been used to connect you with additional and complementary content. This can be accessed via your mobile device when you install the Layar app.

What additional content can be accessed?

In this edition of *Construction site safety* the following content is available for you to access via your mobile device.

- ☑ The CITB online shop.
- ☑ The GE 700 companion website.
- ☑ The new product demonstration video.
- ☑ Toolbox talk instructional videos.

How to install the app

- ☑ Go to the appropriate app store (Apple or Android) and download the Layar app (free of charge) to your mobile phone or tablet.
- ☑ Look out for this logo [right], which indicates that you are on a Layar-friendly page.
- ☑ Open the Layar app and scan the Layar-friendly page.
- ☑ Wait for the page to activate on your device.
- ☑ Touch one of the buttons that have appeared to access additional content.

Where can I find augmented reality in this publication?

The table below identifies the pages in this publication that are compatible with augmented reality and the information that becomes available when an active page is scanned.

GE 700 Section	Location	Content
Box	Cover	Visit the companion website Watch a product demonstration Watch the *Setting out* film Buy related products
I: Supporting information	Cover	Visit the companion website Watch a product demonstration Watch the *Setting out* film Buy related products
A: Legal and management	Cover	Visit the companion website Buy related products Access the 2015 CDM Regulation information page Download the CDM industry guidance for Clients Download the CDM industry guidance for Principal designers Download the CDM industry guidance for Designers Download the CDM industry guidance for Principal contractors Download the CDM industry guidance for Contractors Download the CDM industry guidance for Workers
B: Health and welfare	Cover	Visit the companion website Buy related products
	B01:page 13	Watch a needlestick injuries toolbox talk
	B04: page 36	Watch the ecstasy information film
	B04: page 37	Watch the cocaine information film Watch the heroin information film Watch the LSD information film
	B04: page 38	Watch the cannabis information film
	B06: page 73	Watch an eye protection toolbox talk
	B09: page 122	Access the HSE asbestos web tool
	B11: page 165	Visit the HSE CO awareness page
	B13: page 193	Access the HSE noise exposure demonstration recordings
C: General safety	Cover	Visit the companion website Buy related products
	C06: page 89	Visit the CCSG website Watch the pumping concrete film
D: High risk activities	Cover	Visit the companion website Buy related products
	D02: page 26	Watch the fragile roofs film
	D04: page 60	Watch a working on scaffolds toolbox talk
E: Environment	Cover	Visit the companion website Buy related products
F: Specialist activities	Cover	Visit the companion website Buy related products
G: Checklists and forms	Cover	Visit the companion website Buy related products

Quick reference guide

Contents

Legislation

The following information shows some key legislation that relates to each section of GE 700. This list is not exhaustive but is provided to help navigation of GE 700.

A: Legal and management
Construction (Design and Management) Regulations.
Corporate Manslaughter and Corporate Homicide Act.
Employee Consultation Regulations.
Health and Safety at Work etc. Act 1974.
Health and Safety (Consultation with Employees) Regulations.
Health and Safety (Display Screen Equipment) Regulations.
Health and Safety (Enforcing Authority) Regulations.
Health and Safety (Fees) Regulations.
Health and Safety (Offences) Act.
Management of Health and Safety at Work Regulations.
Occupiers Liability Act.
Reporting of injuries, Diseases and Dangerous Occurrences Regulations.
Safety Representatives and Safety Committee Regulations.
Working Time Regulations.

B: Health and welfare
Chemicals (Hazard information and Packaging for Supply) Regulations.
Control of Asbestos Regulations.
Control of Lead at Work Regulations.
Control of Noise at Work Regulations.
Control of Substances Hazardous to Health Regulations.
Control of Vibration at Work Regulations.
Food Hygiene (England) Regulations.
Health and Safety (First Aid) Regulations.
Manual Handling Operations Regulations.
Personal Protective Equipment at Work Regulations.

C: General safety
Electricity at Work Regulations.
Health and Safety (Safety Signs and Signals) Regulations
Lifting Operations and Lifting Equipment Regulations.
Pressure Systems Safety Regulations.
Provision and Use of Work Equipment Regulations.
Regulatory Reform (Fire Safety) Order.
Supply of Machinery (Safety) Regulations.

D: High risk activities
Confined Spaces Regulations.
Dangerous Substances and Explosive Atmosphere Regulations.
Work at Height Regulations.

E: Environment
Environment Act.
Environmental Permitting (England and Wales) Regulations.
Hazardous Waste (England and Wales) Regulations.
Special Waste Regulations.
Waste Batteries and Accumulators Regulations.
Waste Electrical and Electronic Equipment Regulations.
Waste (England and Wales) Regulations.

F: Specialist activities
Building Act.
Highways Act.
New Roads and Street Works Act.
Railways and Other Guided Transport Systems (Safety) Regulations.

Acronyms

The following list contains some of the acronyms that can be found in common use in the building and construction industry. The list should not be considered as exhaustive.

Abbreviation	Explanation
ACoP	Approved Code of Practice
BS	British Standards
BSI	British Standards Institution
CAA	Construction Awards Alliance
CAWR	Control of Asbestos at Work Regulations
CBH	Constructing Better Health
CDM	Construction (Design and Management) Regulations
CIOB	Chartered Institute of Building
CLWR	Control of Lead at Work Regulations
CMIOSH	Chartered Member of the Institution of Occupational Safety and Health
CONIAC	Construction Industry Advisory Committee
COSHH	Control of Substances Hazardous to Health Regulations
CPA	Construction Plant-hire Association
CPCS	Construction Plant Competence Scheme
CSCS	Construction Skills Certification Scheme
DEFRA	Department for Environment, Food and Rural Affairs
DSEAR	Dangerous Substances and Explosive Atmospheres Regulations
EA	Environment Agency
EMAS	Employment Medical Advisory Service
FASET	Fall Arrest Safety Equipment Training
FMB	Federation of Master Builders
FPA	Fire Protection Association
FRS	Fire and Rescue Service
HASWA or HSWA	Health and Safety at Work etc. Act
HAV	Hand-Arm Vibration
HFL	Highly Flammable Liquid(s)
HSE	Health & Safety Executive
IOSH	Institution of Occupational Safety and Health
ITB	Industry Training Board
ITO	Industry Training Organisation
JIB	Joint Industry Board
LA	Local Authority (ies)
LOLER	Lifting Operations and Lifting Equipment Regulations
LPG	Liquefied Petroleum Gas
LSC	Learning and Skills Council

Abbreviation	Explanation
MHSWR	Management of Health and Safety at Work Regulations
NEBOSH	National Examination Board in Occupational Safety and Health
NVQ	National Vocational Qualification
PPE	Personal protective equipment
PUWER	Provision and Use of Work Equipment Regulations
RIDDOR	Reporting of Injuries, Diseases and Dangerous Occurrences Regulations
RPE	Respiratory protective equipment
SSC	Sector Skills Council
SSP	Site Safety Plus
SVQ	Scottish Vocational Qualification
UKAS	United Kingdom Accreditation Service
WBV	Whole-body vibration
WEL	Workplace exposure limit
WWT	Working Well Together

A

A: Legal and management

A01 Health and safety law

A02 The Health and Safety at Work Act

A03 Construction (Design and Management) Regulations

A04 Health and safety policies

A05 Risk assessments and method statements

A06 Induction and training

A07 Communication with non-English speaking workers

A08 Behavioural safety

A09 Leadership and worker engagement

A

A10 Inspections and audits

A11 Statutory forms, notices and registers

A12 Accident prevention and control

A13 Accident reporting and investigation

B: Health and welfare

B06 Personal protective equipment

B07 Control of substances hazardous to health

B08 Skin protection

B09 Asbestos

C: General safety

C01 Site organisation

C02 Fire prevention and control

C03 Electrical safety

C04 Temporary works

C05 Plant and work equipment

C06 Mobile plant and vehicles

C07 Lifting operations

C08 Lifting equipment

C

D: High risk activities

D05 Fall arrest and suspension equipment

D06 Frame erection

D07 Excavations

D08 Underground and overhead services

D09 Confined spaces

D10 Dangerous substances

E: Environment

E01 Sustainable construction and the environment

E02 Resource efficiency

E03 Waste management

E

E04 Energy management

E05 Water management

E

F: Specialist activities

F01 Street works and road works

F02 Trackside safety

F03 Demolition

F04 Shopfitting and interior contracting

F05 Working over or near to water

F06 Mobile workforce and driver safety

F07 House building

G : Checklists and forms

GA Legal and management

GB Health and welfare

GC General safety

G

G

Health, safety and environment publications

Contents

Overview

CITB is an established source of information and advice on health, safety and the environment within the construction industry. We produce a range of quality publications and resources that provide the construction industry with important and up to date information.

You'll find a format to suit you and your team, including printed books, manuals, DVDs, CD-ROMs, apps, downloads and online publications.

Introduction

Our essential publications are quick and easy-access sources of advice and guidance, providing you with the right tools to keep your site and workforce healthy and safe. We'll also help you to stay up to date with the latest legal obligations.

Our products are designed for:

- ☑ small, medium and large construction companies
- ☑ employees – from operatives to managers
- ☑ colleges and training providers.

We make sense of complicated legislation and advise you on how to manage your health, safety and environment responsibilities.

www.

For further information download our publications catalogue.

Work profitably

Well trained staff working to safe practices are more productive. Let us help you to work profitably.

- ☑ We have competitively priced information for everyone, including managers, operatives, supervisors and trainees.
- ☑ We make sense of complex legislation – making it straightforward to understand and apply.
- ☑ Our training products are flexible to fit in with your business.
- ☑ Friendly and knowledgeable staff will help with your order.

How to order

Our competitively priced publications are easy to order.

www.

Phone: 0344 994 4122
Email: publications@citb.co.uk
Web: www.citb.co.uk/en-GB/HSpublications

CITB core publications

CITB offers a range of publications in various formats, a selection of which are shown below.

Construction site safety 2015 — GE 700/15

GE 700 *Construction site safety* is the only publication that brings together everything you need to know on current health, safety and environmental issues.

- ☑ Essential for managers who work on construction sites and *Site management safety training scheme* (SMSTS) candidates.
- ☑ A supporting information section contains all the information you need to know on how to use GE 700, including a contents and legislation reference guide and the special features contained within the publication.
- ☑ GE 700 has a FREE to access complimentary website (citb.co.uk/GE700companion). This website contains news, updates, links to websites on related topics, industry safety alerts and good practice, making GE 700 a one-stop-shop for the latest advice.
- ☑ It will save you time as all the information you need is in one place.
- ☑ It contains all the guidance you need to stay safe and legal, with simplified legislation and a focus on providing practical guidance, photographs and real case studies.
- ☑ A dedicated section contains checklists and forms, for use on a day-to-day basis, in one place.
- ☑ Augmented reality allows you to use the publication interactively with a smartphone or tablet.

Order code: GE 700/15	Format: Book/printed item	Price: £89.40	Levy registered price: £74.50

Construction site safety 2015 digital editions — GE 700/15

- ☑ Handy for use on and off site.
- ☑ Easy to understand menu and navigation controls.
- ☑ Enhanced keyword search facility with 'search word' highlighted in the text.
- ☑ All of the forms from Section G are included as interactive forms, for you to populate and print copies, as required.
- ☑ Facility to print one page as required. Please note that you are unable to print a full chapter or cut/copy and paste text from the chapters. For those requiring a hard copy version, the full GE 700/15 is most appropriate.

Order code: GE 700/15 CD	Format: CD-ROM	Price: £71.40*	Levy registered price: £59.50*
Order code: GE 700/15 ONLINE	Format: Online	12 month licence price: £59.40*	Levy registered price: £49.50*

*Price excludes VAT

Site supervision simplified 2015 — GE 706/15

GE 706 *Site supervision simplified* provides you with easy to understand information and practical guidance on supervising a site.

- ☑ Essential for site supervisors, front line managers and owners of small construction firms.
- ☑ Each chapter starts with a summary of the employers' responsibilities together with a corresponding checklist for supervisors, to help understand what they should be doing to protect their workforce.
- ☑ Augmented reality allows you to use the publication interactively with a smartphone or tablet.
- ☑ GE 706 is the official reference material for the CITB Site Safety Plus, *Site supervisors' safety training scheme* (SSSTS), a two-day course for first line managers and supervisors.

Order code: GE 706/15 | Format: Book/printed item | Price: £23.40 | Levy registered price: £19.50

Site supervision simplified 2015 digital editions — GE 706/15

- ☑ Handy for use on and off site.
- ☑ Easy to understand menu and navigation controls.
- ☑ Enhanced keyword search facility with 'search word' highlighted in the text.
- ☑ Facility to print one page as required. Please note that you are unable to print a full chapter or cut/copy and paste text from the chapters. For those requiring a hard copy version, the full GE 706/15 is most appropriate.

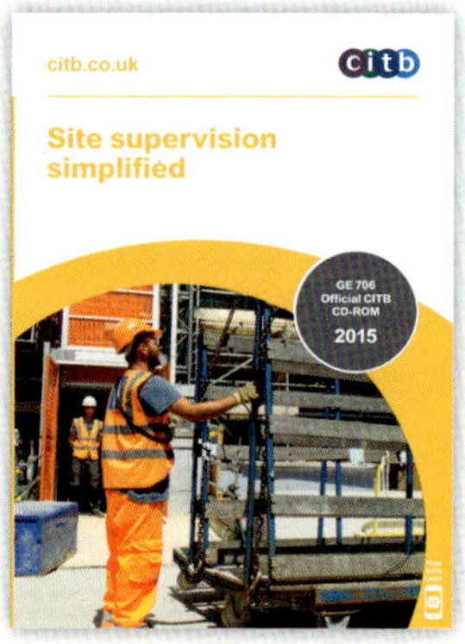

Order code: GE 706/15 CD | Format: CD-ROM | Price: £18.72* | Levy registered price: £15.60*

Order code: GE 706/15 ONLINE | Format: Online | 12 month licence price: £15.00* | Levy registered price: £12.50*

Toolbox talks 2015 — GT 700/15

GT 700 *Toolbox talks* is an important method of both delivering advice on matters of health, safety and the environment, and to engage in discussions to obtain feedback, thus helping to maintain and improve standards. It has been designed to assist supervisors at all levels to prepare and deliver effective toolbox talks on building and construction sites.

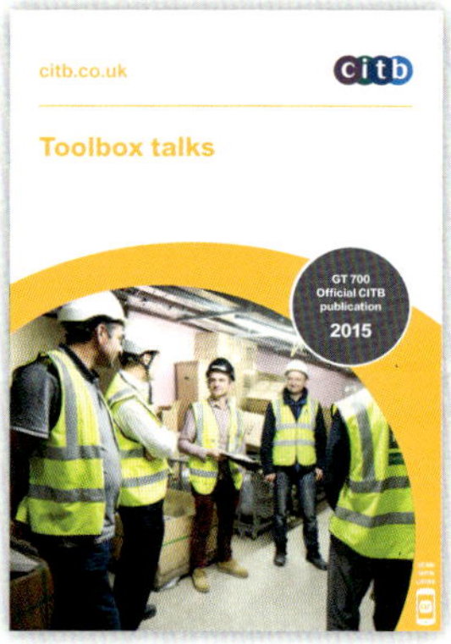

- ☑ Essential for supervisors and operatives.
- ☑ Full colour with photographs.
- ☑ Includes audience-facing images.
- ☑ Contains useful tips to help prepare a talk, a form to record all toolbox talks delivered, a feedback form and a briefing record sheet.
- ☑ Follows the GE 706 structure helping you to cross-reference and prepare for a toolbox talk.
- ☑ Augmented reality allows you to use the publication interactively with a smartphone or tablet.
- ☑ GT 700 *Toolbox talks* and GE 706 *Site supervision simplified* are the official reference material for the CITB Site Safety Plus *Site supervisors' safety training scheme* (SSSTS), a two-day course for first line managers and supervisors.

Order code: GT 700/15 | Format: Book/printed item | Price: £23.40 | Levy registered price: £19.50

*Price excludes VAT

Toolbox talks 2015 digital editions — GT 700/15

- ☑ Contains short presentations to the workforce on essential elements of health, safety and the environment in the building, construction and civil engineering industries.
- ☑ Presentation for the trainer containing detailed prompt notes.
- ☑ Also contains films of three toolbox talks being delivered by real site personnel on a live site.
- ☑ Handy for use on and off site.
- ☑ Easy to understand menu and navigation controls.
- ☑ Enhanced keyword search facility with 'search word' highlighted in the text.
- ☑ Facility to print two pages as required. For those requiring a hard copy version, the full GT 700/15 is most appropriate.

Order code: GE 700/15 CD	Format: CD-ROM	Price: £29.40*	Levy registered price: £24.50*
Order code: GT 700/15 ONLINE	Format: Online	12 month licence price: £23.40*	Levy registered price: £19.50*

Safe start 2015 — GE 707/15

GE 707 *Safe start* provides easy to understand health, safety and environmental information, and practical guidance for operatives.

It has also been written to assist operatives and specialists sitting the CITB *Health, safety and environment test*.

The content follows the test structure, which includes chapters on respiratory risks and environment, as well as individual specialist chapters.

Topics include:

- ☑ accident reporting
- ☑ health and welfare
- ☑ personal protective equipment
- ☑ noise and vibration
- ☑ manual handling
- ☑ fire prevention and control
- ☑ electrical safety
- ☑ working at height.

Each chapter starts with five key things a site or employer should do, and five things operatives should do.

GE 707 is also the official supporting document for the CITB Site Safety Plus one-day health and safety awareness course.

Order code: GE 707/15	Format: Book/printed item	Price: £10.95

Site management safety training scheme — XA6/15

This full colour delegate workbook contains information on the *Site management safety training scheme* (SMSTS) and scheme rules, aims and objectives, delegate exercises and self-study questions.

- ☑ Essential for delegates attending the *Site management safety training scheme* (SMSTS) course.
- ☑ Can be used as an easy reference guide after the course.
- ☑ Designed so that delegates can take ownership of their workbook and use it to make notes.
- ☑ Includes six case study exercises for general construction, house building, civil engineering, demolition, refurbishment and new road and street works.
- ☑ To be used in conjunction with the *Construction site safety* (GE 700) publication.

Order code: XA6/15	Format: Book/printed item	Price: £34.20	Levy registered price: £28.50

*Price excludes VAT

Construction site health, safety and environment auditing system CD SA 03

This CD-ROM will provide you with the forms that you need to carry out compliant health and safety audits and evaluate your company's approach to health and safety step by step, identifying areas for improvement.

- ☑ It is essential for business owners, managers, supervisors and health and safety professionals.

This system helps you to:

- ☑ complete management systems audits and carry out site inspections
- ☑ carry out audits of health and safety procedures and the way they are put into practice
- ☑ customise the audit to your company's specific requirements
- ☑ identify areas for improvement
- ☑ complete action plans
- ☑ monitor improvements in health and safety standards
- ☑ demonstrate that you are fully committed to improving the health and safety of your workforce.

Order code: SA 03 CD | Format: CD-ROM | Price: £29.40* | Levy registered price: £24.50*

Safety critical communication – Toolbox talks GT 701

This pictorial *Toolbox talks* publication has been developed to assist with the communication of critical health and safety messages to operatives with low or limited English, keeping everyone safe on site. It complements the existing *Toolbox talks* (GT 700) publication, and also *Construction site safety* (GE 700) Chapter A07 Communication with non-English speaking workers.

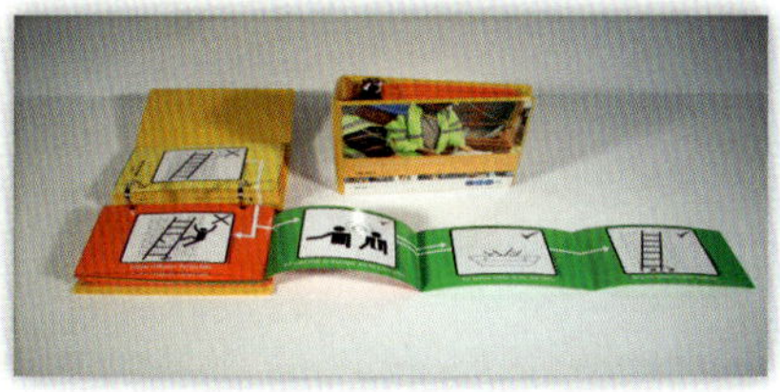

- ☑ Essential for workers with low or limited English.
- ☑ Laminated fold-out cards in two volumes covering hazard, risk and control measures.
- ☑ Can be used in inductions or via toolbox talks.
- ☑ Numbered for ease of use.
- ☑ Strong, long-lasting cards.

Order code: GT 701 | Format: Book/printed item | Price: £60.00 | Levy registered price: £50.00

Risk assessment and method statement manager CD RACD 001/5

This popular CD-ROM enables users to produce, print and store task-specific risk assessments and method statements as required under the Management of Health and Safety at Work Regulations and other legislation.

- ☑ Essential for business owners, managers, supervisors and health and safety professionals.
- ☑ Save and retrieve previous risk assessments and update them as necessary, either within the programme or as standalone Word documents.
- ☑ Pre-populated common hazards and risk controls drop-down menus.
- ☑ Facility to add site specific hazards, methodology and risk controls.
- ☑ Risk assessment and method statement templates, which include:
  - – fields for the signing and dating of each document by hand
  - – the facility for adding footers to all pages
  - – a facility for identifying the 'owner' of each hazard and an action-by date.
- ☑ Option to produce a related or standalone method statement.
- ☑ Includes a *Guide to risk assessment* document, which may be downloaded and printed as a continuing reference.
- ☑ Once installed, the programme functions for one year and then you will need to purchase a replacement. The programme automatically reminds users at the 11-month point that it is due to expire.

Order code: RACD 001/5 | Format: CD-ROM | Price: £29.40* | Levy registered price: £24.50*

*Price excludes VAT

CITB Health, safety and environment test

The CITB *Health, safety and environment test* helps to raise standards across the industry. It ensures that workers have a minimum level of health, safety and environmental awareness before going onto site.

Different tests have been developed to meet the demands of different trades and professions. The following tests are available:

- ☑ operative test
- ☑ specialist tests (visit www.citb.co.uk/hsandetest for more information on the 12 types of specialist test available)
- ☑ managers and professionals test.

Operatives and specialists GT 100/15	Managers and professionals GT 200/15
These revision books contain everything you need to know to book, prepare for and sit the *Health, safety and environment test*. Each book contains all of the knowledge based questions and answers.	
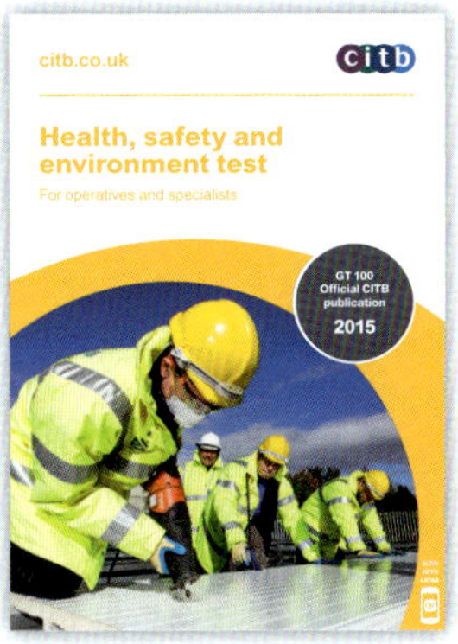	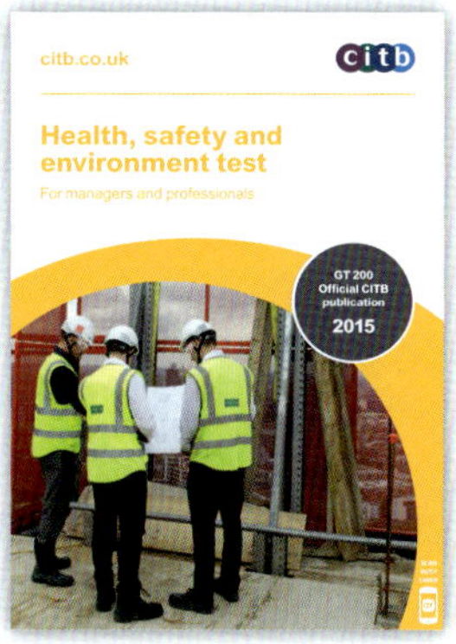
Order code: GT 100/15 Format: Book/printed item Price: £10.95	Order code: GT 200/15 Format: Book/printed item Price: £10.95

Operatives and specialists GT 100/15 digital editions	Managers and professionals GT 200/15 digital editions
These practical revision DVDs provide you with all of the knowledge and information you need to prepare for and sit the *Health, safety and environment test* including: ☑ all the questions and answers ☑ the *Setting out* film on which the behavioural case studies are based ☑ options to revise for the full test or just specific sections, as required ☑ voice-overs in English and Welsh , plus 12 other languages for the Operatives test.	
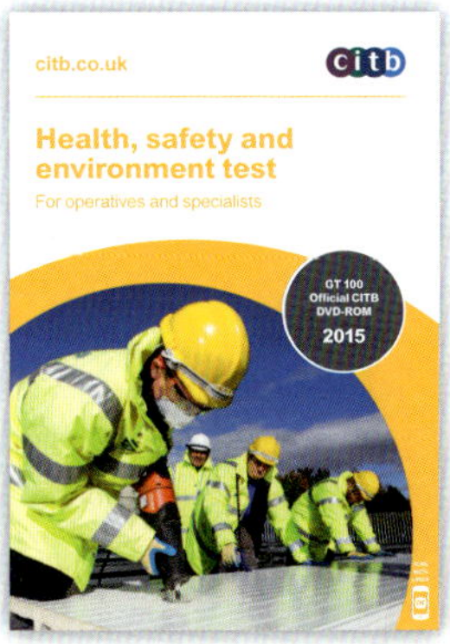	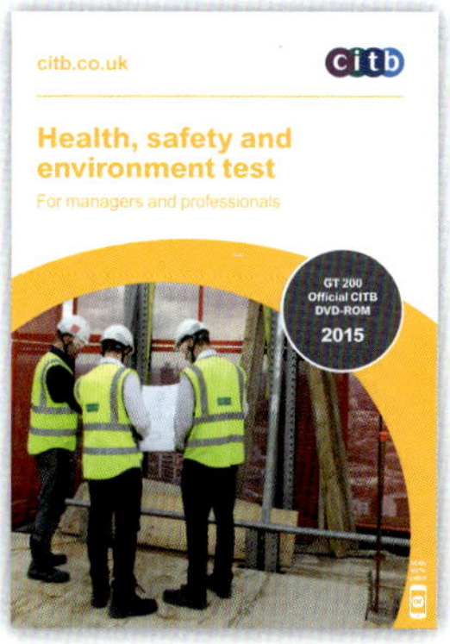
Order code: GT 100/15 DVD Format: DVD Price: £12.42*	Order code: GT 200/15 DVD Format: DVD Price: £12.42*
Order code: GT 100/15 DL Format: Download Price: £11.17*	Order code: GT 200/15 DL Format: Download Price: £11.17*

*Price excludes VAT